THE ASHFORD BOOK OF
DYEING

ANN MILNER STUDIED ART, ceramics and weaving at Coventry Teacher Training College in England. Her weaving tutor was the late Constance Towers.

In 1967 she emigrated to New Zealand and began a study of New Zealand flora for her book on natural dyeing, *Natural Wool Dyes and Recipes*, which was published in 1971.

For three years she was natural dye adviser to 'The Web' magazine published by the New Zealand Spinning, Weaving and Woolcrafts Society. During this period of time she returned to weaving and was invited to exhibit in the Merke Sharpe and Dohme 'Golden Fleece' exhibition.

Study projects on fibres and methods of spinning, which were produced for her tutoring purposes, became the basis for *I Can Spin a Different Thread*, published in 1979.

Ann Milner specializes in handwoven fabrics, using handspun yarns which are dyed and blended from fibre to finished fabrics, designed for clients and galleries. Her current interest is in wall fabrics, which are to look at rather than to wear, and often contain areas of dyed cotton woven into the background.

Ann Milner tutors for the New Zealand Spinning, Weaving and Woolcraft Society, for WEA, and for the Otago Polytechnic.

Streetsongs

The Keytext Program

Louise Matteoni
Wilson H. Lane
Floyd Sucher
Thomas D. Yawkey

Theodore L. Harris, Advisory Author

Harold B. Allen, Linguistic Consultant

THE ECONOMY COMPANY

Oklahoma City   Indianapolis   Orange, CA

Design and Art Direction: James Stockton

Cover Illustration: Pat Maloney

The Keytext Program was developed with the participation of Kraft and Kraft, Stow, Massachusetts.

Permission to use or adapt copyrighted material appearing in this book is gratefully acknowledged on pages 159 and 160, which are hereby made a part of this copyright page.

ISBN 0-8332-1054-8

THE ECONOMY COMPANY, Educational Publishers
1901 North Walnut   Oklahoma City, Oklahoma 73125

Contents

Runways

Waterways

Give and Take

The Boy Who Wouldn't Talk

We work with words.

sorry   thirty   history

salty   rocky   eighty

saying   watching   waiting

twister   longer   leader

showed   talked   waited

Sound the words.

hurry

delivery

learning

teacher

wished

Sight words.

Carlos and Angel Vega

came from Puerto Rico.

8

Carlos Doesn't Like Words

Carlos Vega came from Puerto Rico with his family. They had an apartment near a park. Carlos did like to walk to the park. But he didn't like the city much.

His little brother, Angel, was very happy to hurry to school. But each day Carlos walked to school slowly. He was in no hurry to get there.

One day as he walked to school, Carlos wished he was back in Puerto Rico!

In Puerto Rico all the books were in Spanish, and he had learned to read some of them. But in the city, he couldn't read any of the books. Learning to read here was harder than learning to read in Puerto Rico.

9

Carlos wished he didn't have to use words at all. Sometimes he didn't use words, and he got along fine.

As he walked, he said to himself, "I don't really need to say or read anything, and I'm not going to. I'll nod for yes. I can show people the things I want, and I'll draw pictures."

When Carlos got home, he made a picture of a delivery truck. The next day, he put the picture in his pocket to take to school.

Carlos put the picture up for the boys and girls to see. Everyone said it was very good. "Is it a delivery truck?" asked his teacher, Mrs. Dawn. Carlos gave a nod. "When did you draw it?" Mrs. Dawn asked.

Carlos didn't say anything.

"Did you do the picture Monday?" the teacher asked.

Carlos gave a nod, put the picture back in his pocket, and went to his seat with a smile. "It's easy to get along without talking," he said to himself.

Mr. and Mrs. Vega and Angel began to feel bad. Each day, Mrs. Vega asked Carlos, "Do you feel like talking today?"

Each day, Carlos would just smile.

We work with words.

movement   agreement

deeds   cords   beasts

flippers   flames   eggs

wildest   thickest   nearest

Sound the words.

pavement

bumps

letters

quickest

Will Carlos Talk Again?

The next Friday, when Carlos was going home after school, he met a boy.

The boy said, "I heard you come by. Can you help me out? Would you walk me home?"

Carlos gave the boy a nod and a smile, but he didn't understand.

"My mother can't come for me today," the boy said. "My name is Ricky."

Carlos shook Ricky's hand.

12

"Do you know the quickest way to my house?" Ricky asked.

Carlos didn't say anything.

"Why don't you say something! Will you let me tell you the quickest way?"

Carlos gave a nod.

"If you're not going to talk to me, I'll wait for another boy!" Ricky was mad.

Carlos didn't understand.

"Where do you live?" Ricky asked after a while. He was not mad now.

Carlos made a map on the pavement with some chalk.

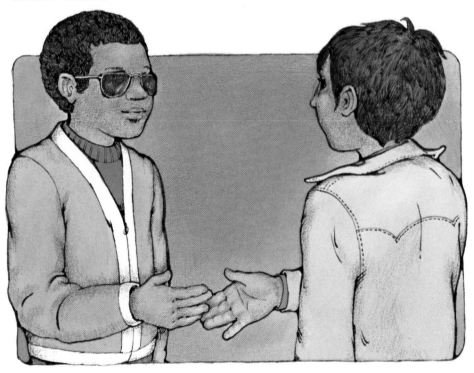

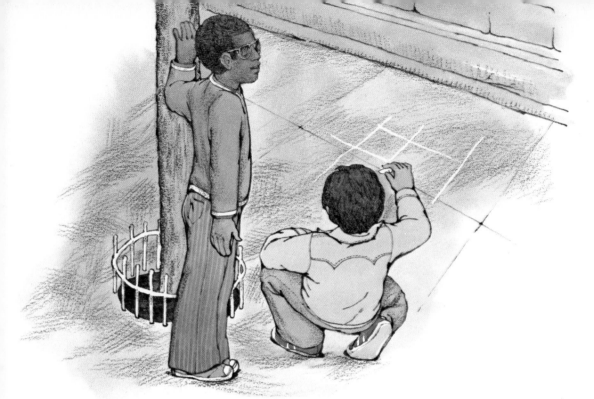

Ricky said, "I know you wrote something. I heard the sound of the chalk on the pavement. But I can't see it. I can't see you or anything."

Carlos became very still. This was the first boy he ever met who couldn't see. He wanted to know why. But he would have to ask Ricky to find out. Finally he said, "Why can't you see?"

"My eyes don't work," Ricky said. "Boy, I'm happy you're talking to me!"

"I'll talk to you. My name is Carlos," Carlos said. He shook Ricky's hand again.

As they walked, Ricky asked, "If you can talk, why don't you talk to everyone?"

"There are too many words. And I don't like some of them," Carlos said.

"You can tell me some Spanish words," said Ricky. "Then I'll say them in Spanish, too."

At Ricky's apartment, Carlos saw a big book with no letters on the page. It had bumps instead. "What is this book with bumps?" Carlos asked.

Ricky said, "The bumps stand for letters. I read by feeling them."

"I like feeling letters," Carlos said.

"Say, I have a great idea, Carlos!" Ricky said. "Sometimes on Saturday, I go with my father on a train to a park. Would you like to go with us?"

Carlos said, "I'll have to ask my mother and father."

"You mean you're going to talk to them?" Ricky asked.

"I don't know yet," Carlos said.

"I hope you ask them," Ricky said.

When Carlos got to his house, he walked up the steps very slowly. He didn't know if he wanted to talk to his family or not. He was afraid to start talking again. Maybe everyone would make fun of him.

"What is in that bag?" Angel asked when Carlos came in. "A book," he said, and looked at the family. No one said a word. They didn't make fun of him. Angel had a big smile on his face.

"It's Ricky's. I met him today," Carlos said. It felt funny to talk again, but it felt good, too. "I have a lot to tell you about Ricky. First, there is the book. And me going home with him. And the park. Can I go to the park with him?"

"Boy!" said Mr. Vega. "One thing at a time."

Let's Talk about Talking

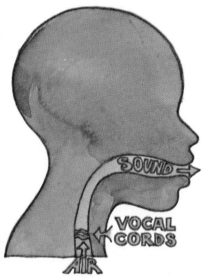

We work with words.

phase   photo

David   bugle   level

north   force   corn

brothers   broke

finish   brushed   share

eardrum   somewhere   seaweed

barefoot   wheelchair

Sound the words.

telephone

vocal

cords

vibrate

shape

earpiece

mouthpiece

metal

Sight words.

There are air spaces in your mouth called cavities.

You use your tongue to make sounds when you talk.

17

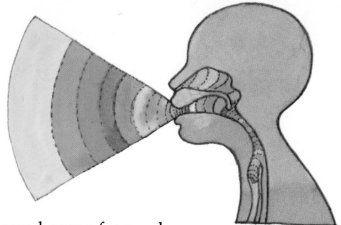

Where does the sound come from when you talk?

You know you breathe in air. You know you breathe air out, too. The air you breathe out makes you talk.

In your throat you have vocal cords. They are in the shape of lips. When air goes between the vocal cords, it makes them vibrate. This means they move back and forth quickly.

There are spaces in your throat, mouth, and nose. These spaces are called cavities. When your vocal cords vibrate, the air in these cavities begins to vibrate, too. You can change the shape of the cavities with your tongue and lips. When you change the shape of a space, you change the way that air vibrates in it. This is how you make each different sound when you talk or sing. You can see this for yourself.

Just say an "ah" sound, like the one you hear in "father." Move your lips into a round "o" shape. Did you hear the sound change? Did it become a long "o" sound? You made the shape of the space in your mouth change. You can do this with your tongue. Say "ah" again. Now change the "ah" quickly to a long "e" sound. Did you feel your tongue move? You needed to move your tongue to make the shape of the space inside your mouth different. That made the sound you heard different.

But why do your ears hear the sound? Remember, when your vocal cords vibrate, air in the cavities, or spaces in your mouth, nose, and throat, begins to vibrate, too. Everything in the reach of your voice begins to vibrate when you speak.

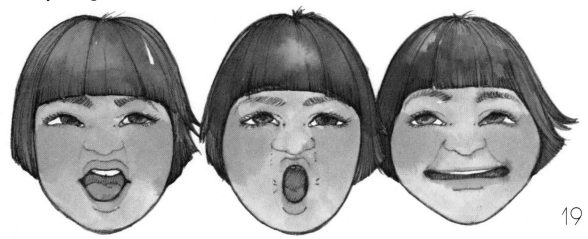

Air that vibrates also makes a telephone work. When you speak into a telephone, your voice makes air vibrate, and the air goes into the mouthpiece.

There is a metal disk in the earpiece of a telephone. The metal disk in the earpiece vibrates when sound from another telephone comes into it.

Just like the disk in the mouthpiece, the disk in the earpiece makes the air vibrate.

Then air makes your eardrum vibrate, and when your eardrum vibrates, you hear a voice on the telephone.

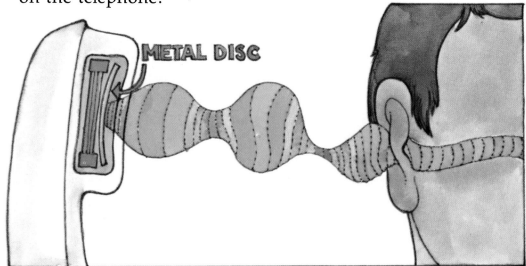

METAL DISC

Talking Animals

We work with words.

chop arch chained

pilot Lewis polar

turtles tadpole surprise

miles flames

shouted pulled packed

layer washer twisters

Sound the words.

chimp

human

sentence

shapes

showed

teachers

Only people can really talk, but there are one or two animals who have learned to use words. One was a chimp called Washoe. It wasn't easy for her, as it is for a human, because a chimp can't use its tongue and lips as well as we do. But a chimp can use its hands, and that's what Washoe learned to do.

Her teachers showed her how to make different shapes with her hands. She learned to make each hand shape stand for a word. Here are some of the hand shapes Washoe learned:

More

Food

Dirty

Listen

Washoe, touch Ann.   Ann, touch Washoe.

Her teachers showed Washoe how to put words together to make a sentence. At first, Washoe didn't understand that if you change the order of words in a sentence, the sentence means something different. Let's say you made this sentence with your hands: "Washoe, touch Ann." Washoe would do as you said. Now, let's say you said, "Ann, touch Washoe." What would Washoe do? She would touch Ann again. She wouldn't understand that the second sentence means something different.

Washoe was a very smart chimp. She learned to use words and to put them together. But she didn't learn as much as a human child does. As far as we know, only people can talk.

23

TONGUE TWISTERS

Now you know that only people, and not animals, can talk. How good are you at it? Try to trip these terrible twisters off your tongue:

Suddenly, she saw some short, silly sharks.

The robot watched Rose while she rested.

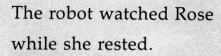

Four fine fish found a perfect, fresh frog Friday.

The weather report warned of terrible twisters Tuesday.

Monsters of the Sea

Meet Nessie!

We work with words.

unafraid unhurt

apart afire

hello Griffin balloon

eagle ankle turtle

Oregon horrible deliver

shouted touch cloudy

fell hunt mad

graph phone photo

squeeze squeak

Sound the words.

unknown

alive

bottom

bubbles

dinosaur

thousands

hump

photograph

squid

unable

Sight word.

Is <u>Nessie</u> a monster?

26

Some people say that the photograph on page 26 is a picture of a real monster. They call her Nessie! People say they have seen her in Loch Ness. Loch Ness is a lake in Scotland.

Some scientists have gone to the lake to try to learn more about this unknown monster. Scientists can't catch her, but they have been able to take a photograph of something that looks like a monster in Loch Ness. Someone took this photograph from a long way off. Do you think it really is a monster?

Some girls and boys, who live near Loch Ness, saw Nessie in the lake one day.

One boy said it may have been a log far away from him, but it looked as if it swam slowly across the lake. There was one big hump and another small hump, which may have been its head.

One other child saw a monster with a head like a brown snake, humps, and a tail.

28

There was a big splash as it went underwater. The monster that another child saw was alive. It looked like a fish with two humps and a tail.

No one has real proof that there are monsters in Loch Ness. Scientists try to get a good photograph of Nessie under the water. The dark water in the lake hides things well. The monster must come very close to the camera, or they can't get a good picture. Scientists do take a kind of sound picture. This sound picture may have found some big animal in the lake. But we are unable to tell if it is Nessie.

Is Nessie a Dinosaur?

Thousands and thousands of years ago, there were many dinosaurs in the sea and on land. We know about dinosaurs from the fossils of their bones that we have found. Fossils are "pictures" made in mud that have become rock. We can see these very clearly.

People who study fossils have a good idea of what some of the sea dinosaurs looked like.

Many people think that Nessie looks a lot like a dinosaur. Could a kind of unknown dinosaur family still be alive at the bottom of Loch Ness?

Is Nessie a Squid?

Some people think that Nessie may be a kind of squid that hides under the sea. A squid has a big body with no bones. It can move quickly and leaves a wave in the water. Since it has no bones, a squid can make its body look different.

Is Nessie a Log, a Boat, or Mud?

When the day is not very clear, a log can look like a sea monster.

A boat on the other side of the lake may be Nessie. Many people have seen the wave in back of the boat.

The bottom of Loch Ness is full of mud and dead leaves. When dead leaves and mud move to the top of the water, they make bubbles. The mud and bubbles are what other people call a monster.

Is there a Loch Ness monster? The answer is unknown. What do you think is in Loch Ness?

Sea Monsters Old and New

below	beside	belonged		beware
	pair	chair	stair	hair
	turtle	bugle	ankle	horrible
	bands	drums	deeds	meters
		bore	core	shore
		sway	swamp	swam

Sea monsters have been talked about for many, many years. It is hard to tell which tales were true and which were not.

Sea monsters in the old days were, for the most part, not very nice. People who went to sea were afraid their ships would run into a horrible sea monster that would then eat them all alive.

Ships had a person made of wood on the front. This person had open eyes, so it could watch day and night for all sea monsters and keep the ship safe.

If you look at this old map, you can find where sea monsters were seen or said to live. People knew that they should beware of these places.

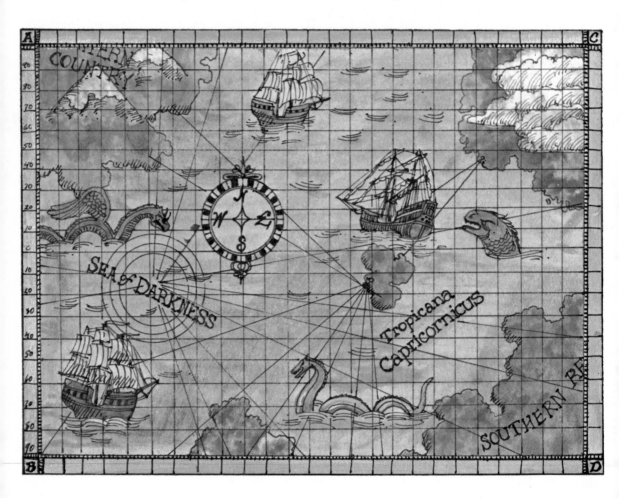

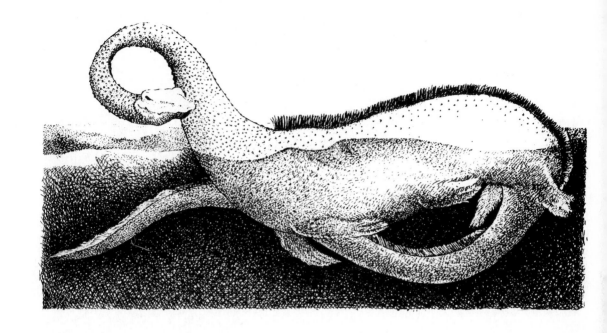

A man once found a strange, dead beast on a shore. This beast had a small head, a long neck, six legs, and a very long tail. It was about 17 meters long (about 51 feet). Thick hair ran from the bottom of its neck to the end of its tail. The hair could shine in the dark. Scientists came to study the strange sea beast. It was new to them. No one could say just what the animal was.

A sea monster was seen off the shore of the United States. Many, many people saw this monster as it swam up and down the shore. They said it was about 20 meters long (about 60 feet). It swam very fast. It could turn quickly.

For a long time, this monster came to visit a town on the shore each summer. It did nothing, but the people of the town did not feel safe.

They set out to hunt and kill the monster. One man told the paper how he had been on the hunt when the monster swam close to his boat. He knew that he hit the beast in the head. The sea monster began to turn around. The man knew the monster was about to come after him. But he saw the monster go down and swim under his boat. The sea monster must not have felt a thing. No one could kill that monster. After a while, the sea monster did not come back.

For years, tales were told about the horrible kraken. It was said to be round and had many arms. It could be as big as 100 meters (about 300 feet). People said the kraken would kill a man on ship with a horrible hug of one of its arms. Kraken would come upon ships on the open sea and pull them down into the water as it swam for the bottom of the ocean.

Many people said there was no such thing as a kraken. It was just a silly sea monster story. But in 1861, a ship was able to bring back an arm of a large kraken, or a squid as they are now called.

How many other sea monsters may just be big sea animals that we know about today? Which sea monster tales are true, which are part true, and which have just been made up?

Are You Hungry?

hunger   danger   hung

rung   hang   drink

marked   frowned   belonged

known   knock

workers   nearer   burner

kites   mate   laid

fireplace   earthworm   somewhere

turtles   welcome

dangerous

hungry

crawled

knocked

deeper

dove

everywhere

snorkel

<u>Keoki</u> lives in <u>Hawaii</u>.

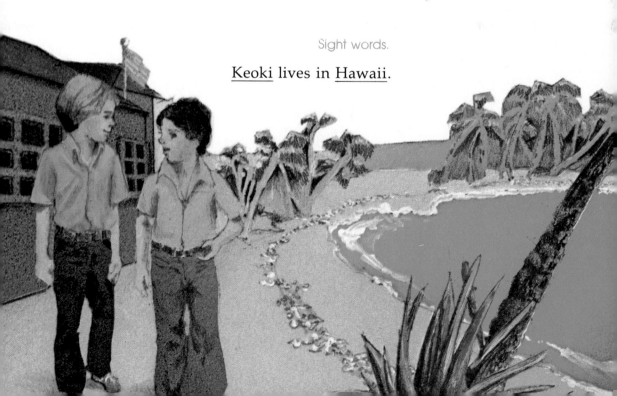

Ken, the "new boy," came from Detroit. Days went by before anyone in his new class talked to him. He felt strange here in Hawaii.

Keoki came up to him after school and asked, "Did you swim much in Detroit?"

"Of course I did," said Ken. "I was on the Detroit YMCA team."

"Good," said Keoki. "We can skindive together. Meet me at Blue Beach tomorrow. If we get hungry, we can catch an octopus. Out here, we dive in the ocean where the animals live, not in a pool. See you tomorrow."

"An octopus?" Ken asked himself. "Isn't that dangerous?"

The next day, Ken met Keoki at Blue Beach.

"The water is warm," said Keoki. "I think we'll see a lot of fish today."

The two boys walked into the water. The water felt good around their legs. Each boy pulled his mask and snorkel down over his face. Then they dove into the water.

They swam out into the ocean for a while. Then they took a deep breath and dove under water. They came up for a breath of air and dove again.

Everywhere Ken looked, he saw tiny fish. Everywhere he swam, plants brushed his skin. Ken knew some plants were dangerous, and he watched out for those.

Suddenly, a big fish knocked against the skin on his arm. Ken pulled away quickly, but the big fish swam on.

41

"We'll skindive for octopus tomorrow," said Keoki. "I think you'll like that."

As Ken walked home, he didn't feel well. He didn't want the arms of an octopus around his body. What if it wouldn't let go?

That night in bed, Ken dreamed that an octopus knocked him down and had its arms around his body. The arms crawled up and down his back. Ken was out of breath. His snorkel and mask were knocked off. This was dangerous.

"Help! Help, Keoki."

Ken woke up. He looked around in the dark.

"I must have dreamed everything," he said. Then he fell asleep.

42   The next day, Ken met Keoki at the beach.

"We'll dive in deeper water today," said Keoki. "I think we'll find an octopus there."

Would Keoki get mad if he said he didn't want to go? Ken put on his mask and snorkel, but he felt afraid.

The two boys swam out into the deeper water. Then they dove down to the bottom. Suddenly, Keoki reached under a rock. He pulled his hand out. The octopus on Keoki crawled up and down his arm.

Ken couldn't believe how small and ugly it was. The boys swam back to the beach.

Keoki gave the octopus to Ken. It crawled up and down his arm. Ken looked at the octopus, and the octopus looked back. Its eyes looked mad.

"What do you think of an octopus now that you have met one?" asked Keoki. "Are you hungry?"

"No, I'm not hungry at all," said Ken.

Not Me

The Slithergadee has crawled out of
    the sea.
He may catch all the others, but he
    won't catch me.
No, you won't catch me, old Slithergadee,
You may catch all the others, but you wo —

44

At Home in the City

We work with words.

dare   rare

Sound the word.

share

Sight word.

That <u>building</u> is in the city.

I live on the third floor of my building, and I have to share a room with my brother and my sister. Sometimes, I can't get to sleep because they like to talk so much. My mother will tell them to keep still, but in a while they will just start up again. Sometimes, they pick on me. If I ever have my own room, they will have to ask me to come in.

47

My grandmother came to live with us, and she and my sister share a room. My grandmother can't speak much English, so I help her when she goes to the store. One time she got a can of food for the dog, but it was really chicken soup! When the weather is warm, I like to sit with Grandmother on the front steps of our building and talk. I help teach her English, so she can talk to all of our friends, too.

We Want Our Park!

My teacher said to write a story that is happy or sad. Well, this story is happy and sad. It took place last summer.

The best place to play ball near my house was the
lot on Green Street. There were no houses close by
and no windows to break. The only building near
the lot was shut up. Almost every day, we would go
over to the lot to hit a ball around. Then one day at
about ten, Raúl ran over to my apartment.

"Have you been over to the lot today?" he asked.
His face looked hot, and he talked fast. "There are
walls and workers, and a scoop... and... Come
on!" he said.

I ran to the lot with Raúl. Rosa and Bob were
there, too.

Rosa was mad. "What about our ball park? I don't want to see a scoop or pipes or beams," she said.

Raúl talked to two workers. They said they were going to build a tall apartment building.

"Great," said Rosa. "A big, steel, and concrete building, set in our ball park. Just great!"

Little by little, the building went up. The scoop made a big hole in the ground. The concrete was put in the hole for the basement. Then the steel beams were put up. Bob, Rosa, and I sat on some pipes and watched the workers build concrete walls. Piles of windows were set into place.

"If I could, I'd lift that building over about 100 yards. Yes, 100 yards would be just fine. Then we could still have a place to play," said Rosa.

One day, the new building was done. The workers began to take away the leftover pipes and beams. Rosa, Raúl, and I were walking to another park. We saw some people looking at a map. They were talking about that old, shut-up building close by. As we went by the workers, Rosa asked, "Ready to put up another apartment?"

"That old building is not safe," said one of the workers. "The city is going to build a park. It will have a big slide and a place to play ball."

Now you know the happy part of the story. We have a great, new ball park to play in.

Homes You Don't See Every Day

This town was made into the side of a hill many years ago.

Someday, many houses will get their heat from the sun. It will make the house very warm, and the sun is free, so it will cost less.

If you want a warm house in the woods, this is it. It's made from trees and nails, because that's all that is needed.

How would you like to live in a house like this? If you want fish for dinner, just let a line down from your front door.

A New Home in the West

We work with words.   Sound the words.

they've   you've   we've

sorry   channel   pebbles   allow

waited   brushed   drifted   belonged

record   solo   pilot   wagon

hello

Sight word.

The family was very quiet.

55

There Could Be Trouble

Long ago, a wagon train went slowly west. In it were people who wanted to begin a new life. One wagon belonged to the Johnsons, a free black family. They had been working on a farm that was not their farm. Now they were going west to settle on a farm of their own.

The two Johnson children, Mary, who was twelve, and James, who was ten, were quiet. They sat behind their parents in the wagon and looked out at the miles of land.

"Mary, are you afraid?" asked James.

"Of course," said Mary. "We've come all these miles to a new place. Even Ma and Pa are afraid. I heard them say so. We don't know if we're wanted out there or what it's like."

The children were quiet again. Then they went up front with their parents.

The wagon train went on west, day after day. It was a long, hard trip. Then it was time for the wagon train to stop and for each family to go its own way.

The Johnsons went on alone with the wagon and horse that belonged to them. They went by a man who was about to chop wood in front of his cabin. Mary and James called out a hello to him, but the man did not answer their hello. He just looked at them.

"Ma, why doesn't that man say hello?" asked James.

"We've got to be quiet now, James," she said. "When we're on our own land, things will be different."

Soon the family came to a perfect place to build a cabin. Trees were all around them for miles, and a small river ran under the trees.

The Johnsons would begin to chop down trees for a cabin the next day. But first, they would have to sleep.

That night, the family jumped up as something hard hit the side of the wagon. Mr. Johnson went outside. He found a big rock. The words on it said, "Go back where you came from." They did not sleep very well that night.

The next day, the family began to chop wood for their cabin. A man came up to the wagon. He didn't look like a friend.

"I live just over the river," he said. "I came to warn you to leave. I don't want any black people near me. I have friends who feel the same. You just better go back where you came from. If you don't, there could be trouble."

"I don't understand," said Mr. Johnson. "What trouble are you talking about?"

The man on the horse said, "I won't allow black people to settle next door to me. And I'm not the only one. We won't stand for it!"

"What are we going to do, Pa?" asked James. "We can't go back, can we, Ma?"

Mrs. Johnson looked at the man. "We've come too far to go back," she said.

"I don't know what we can do," said Mr. Johnson. "Get in the wagon, children. Let's go."

Welcome to Our Town

Mr. Johnson began to drive again. When they had left the white man behind, he looked at his family.

"Children," he said, "that man doesn't want to live next door to us, but he can't send us back. We are free people."

60

Later that day, the Johnsons came to a river. When they had gone across, they met a tall black man.

"Hello, I'm George Bush," he said. "Welcome to our town. There is good, rich land along this river. And it's a good place to raise children."

"This does look like what we want," Mr. Johnson said with a smile.

"Good," Mr. Bush said. "The people here will welcome you with open arms. Tomorrow we will help you build a log cabin."

The next day, the people began to come. Some were black, and some were white, and each had built a log cabin before.

A group of men went out to cut trees. First, they would cut a notch into a tree, then chop it down. Other men would pile up the logs and take them to where the cabin was being built.

Four long logs were laid on the ground in a big square. A notch was cut into each end of the logs. The logs would fit together where each notch was. Other logs were laid on top of these four to make the walls of the house. Next, a space would be cut out of the walls to make a door. Mary and James watched with a smile as the logs took on the shape of a house.

Another group of people built a big fireplace and chimney at one end of the house. The fireplace would cook the food and heat the house, and the chimney would let the smoke out.

Others had to finish the walls. Then it was time to raise the roof. Big poles were laid across the top of two walls. Smaller poles were put into the spaces between the big poles. The men on the roof had to nail the shingles over the poles. The shingles would keep the rain out.

The children worked, too. They would mix the mud and clay and then push it into the spaces between the logs. The mud and clay would get hard and help keep the cabin warm.

When the men were just about to finish the cabin, it was time for dinner.

Everyone ate a lot. Later, some people began to play music, and everyone began to sing along.

A woman built a fire with a big pile of wood that would not smoke too much. A man told them all a story as they sat around the fire. Then it was time for people to finish talking and go home.

"What a fine welcome," said Mr. Johnson with a big smile. "This will be a good home for us."

Then the family was alone. They could go into their new home for the first time.

Solo

I'll Fly Alone

We work with words.

replace   recall

dragon   relay   eagle

Sound the words.

return

pilot

record

All her life, Sheila Scott has looked for adventure. If someone tells her that something can't be done, that only makes her want to try very hard to do it.

Sheila's father knew she was like that, even as a little girl. If her father would tell her that she was afraid to get on a wild ride at the fair, that was the ride she would take.

If they went for a swim, her father would tell her that it was too hard for a little girl like her to jump into the pool. So, of course, Sheila would jump in. He always knew Sheila would try it if he said it was too hard.

But those were small adventures when you think of the great adventure she had when she was six years old. She got to ride in a plane.

Sheila could always remember that adventure, and one day, many years later, she said she wanted to learn to fly.

Sheila said this to friends who didn't believe her. They said it would be too hard for her to learn to fly. This made Sheila want to fly more than ever, so she got someone to teach her how to fly. Then she got a plane and a paper that said she could be a pilot.

Sheila wanted still another adventure, so she took her plane to a race. There, she won her very first race. After that, she won many more races.

Then Sheila had an idea for a big, big adventure. She would fly alone around the world!

After a lot of work, Sheila was ready to leave England, the country that was her home.

At last she took off. She had many adventures on her trip around the world. Sometimes dangerous things happened, but she did not quit. After setting a world record, she made a safe return to England.

That record was for the longest plane trip by one person around the world. Since she had a great adventure and a world record to remember, she could have quit, but she never did. After that trip, she made one trip after another. Sometimes she would set a new record before her return to England.

Sheila Scott has done many things that other people have never done, and she has had some of the great adventures of our time.

My Solo Adventure

We work with words.

scream scrape screen

somewhere earthworm

cliff skull pond

eagle wizard dragon

Sound the words.

scrap

downtown

kid

relax

solo

70

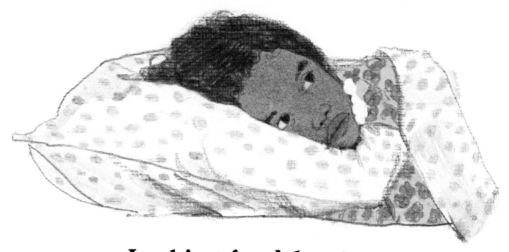

Looking for Adventure

"Well, that's it," said Elaine as she put down the book she was reading. "If Sheila Scott can have a solo adventure, so can I!"

"Elaine," said her mother as she looked into the room. "Don't you think it's late for you to be up? Why don't you finish reading that book tomorrow?"

"Oh," said Elaine, "I've read the whole book. It was very good."

"Well," said her mother, "go to sleep now. You've been reading too long."

"I'll try," said Elaine. "But I've got a lot on my mind, and I can't seem to relax."

"Try hard," said her mother. "Good night."

"Good night," said Elaine.

71

But when her mother left the room, Elaine could not sleep. She was trying to plan a solo adventure. It was something she had to do.

"Some of my older friends think I'm a kid," said Elaine. "Well, I'll show them. I'll have a great solo adventure. They won't call me a kid again."

Elaine did not know how she would get there or where she would go. But this didn't mean she was going to scrap the whole idea. "I don't have a plane like Sheila Scott had. Man, I don't even have a bike. But I do have feet. I'll use my feet," said Elaine.

Now where would she go? "I've heard people talk about downtown," she said. "They say downtown is where it's at. Downtown is where I'll go. Boy! That would be a great adventure!"

Then Elaine began to think. She knew the city was a big place. She knew the walk downtown would be long. She could ride a train, but she didn't have any money.

Elaine began to get nervous about her adventure. Did she have to scrap the whole idea?

"I've got to relax," said Elaine. "I can't scrap this idea. I won't let it scare me. I won't let anything scare me again."

Elaine knew that by now it must be very late. She was afraid that she would always be just a kid. Elaine did not sleep very well that night.

Alone Downtown

It was Saturday. Elaine was walking up and down her block. She wanted to get in shape for her adventure.

"Boy! I feel out of energy," said Elaine. "I've only walked up and down my block five times. How will I make it all the way downtown? This street is hot. I need something to drink already."

She saw her older friends on her block. They called, "Kid, what are you doing?"

"Nothing much," Elaine said. She would not tell them about her adventure yet. She wouldn't tell them about it at all if it didn't happen.

As she sat down on her front steps, she met her grandmother, who was on her way to their apartment. "Elaine," her grandmother said, "It's late, but here is the money I told you I would give you for doing so well in school."

Elaine gave her grandmother a big hug. And when her grandmother went inside, Elaine said, "Money! This is great! Who needs to walk? I'll use this money to ride the train downtown."

Elaine could see the big clock on a tall building. It was ten o'clock. Suddenly, she felt better. "Ten o'clock," said Elaine. "I can leave now and be back before dark."

Elaine ran to the train stop. It was just up the block. Then she ran down the steps. "Now," she said, "I've got to look at the map to find the shortest way downtown."

While Elaine was looking at the map, an older boy said, "Can I help you, kid?"

"No," said Elaine. "I don't need any help. And I'm not a kid."

"Oh," said the boy as he walked away.

TO
ALL
TRAINS

77

Elaine knew now she had to make this adventure happen. She looked at the map again. "I get it," she said. "I'll take this train. Then I'll change to the D train that goes to downtown. That will be the shortest way to go downtown."

Soon Elaine was on the train. Then she was on the D train. She couldn't wait for her stop to come.

Finally, a voice called, "Times Square." Elaine had to push her way out of the train car. She ran to the street. "Man!" she said as she looked around. "Downtown is where it's at!" All around her, she saw people, stores, and even a sandwich shop. "May I have a chicken sandwich and something to drink?" she asked the man in the sandwich shop.

"You got the money for a sandwich and a drink?" he asked. "Let me see it."

"Here it is," she said. The man took almost all of her money. "Boy, a chicken sandwich must cost a lot downtown. I can just make it home on what I have left."

Elaine ate her sandwich as she walked. She wanted to see downtown. She walked up and down the street.

"I need a rest," Elaine said. "Too bad I don't have my front steps to sit on. This street is hot." Elaine sat on the curb.

She said to herself, "My feet don't feel good. I must rest them. I wish I had my front steps to sit on, too." Elaine did not look very happy.

She heard a voice say, "Are you okay?" Elaine saw a woman in a car. At first, she wanted to say, "No, I need help."

But then, she began to think. She had made the trip all alone. So she felt bad. She knew she could return home. It would be great to finish this adventure alone!

Elaine felt full of energy. She got up and said, "Yes, I'm okay. As a matter of fact, I was just on my way home."

"And after this great adventure, no one can call me just a kid again," she said to herself as she walked to the train.

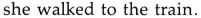

Once a Frog

Jerome

We work with words.

trial	poem	helium
bugle	relay	eagle
dizzy	jazz	lizard
skull	frogs	cliff
edges	else	France
ninety	history	eighty

Sound the words.

giant

dragon

wizard

pond

prince

sorry

Sight words.

He was <u>busy</u>

burning the <u>garbage</u>.

In a pond one day, a frog by the name of Jerome was eating bugs when a wizard came by.

"Hello, old wizard," Jerome said.

The wizard didn't like to be called a wizard. He looked at Jerome with a mean smile. "It's not good to call a person a wizard," he said.

"Well, I'm sorry," said Jerome. "Very sorry."

"I could turn you into something terrible," the wizard said. "But I think I'll turn you into a prince."

"Well, I don't mind," Jerome said.

"We'll see," said the wizard with a laugh. And he put his black stick up in the air and began to sing a strange song.

"Am I a prince now?" Jerome asked.

"Of course you are," said the wizard with a laugh.

"But I don't feel like a prince," Jerome said.

"Oh, you will," said the wizard.

"You will. Just go into town and see what I mean."

So Jerome did as the wizard said. When he came to town, he said, "Hello. I'm the new prince who does princely deeds."

The people had to laugh because they saw that he was just a frog. But they said to Jerome, "So you're a prince who does princely deeds? How would you like to do some for us?"

"I'd be happy to," said Jerome.

"Good," the people said. "Now, the first thing we want you to do is get rid of a terrible, giant crow who has been eating up all our corn." Then they took Jerome to where the corn was green in the sun, and they left him to wait for the crow.

Soon a giant crow landed and began to eat the corn.

"Stop!" Jerome shouted. "Stop eating the corn. It's bad to eat corn that you did not grow."

"Well, I know," said the crow. "But I'm a giant, and it takes a lot to make me full. Also, I'm afraid that everyone is going to eat up all the corn before I do. Wouldn't you like to eat some of this good corn?"

"Not me," Jerome said. "I'd just as soon eat bugs. And I will never ever eat any corn. How about that?"

"Why, that's just fine," said the crow.

"I also know at least six snakes, twice that many fish, and every frog I can think of," Jerome said. "And I know for a fact that many other animals would be happy never to eat corn."

"Great!" shouted the giant crow. And off it went.

After that, Jerome went back to the town and told the people that the crow wouldn't be eating all their corn anymore, but just some of it.

The people said, "That's fine. Would you like to do another princely deed?"

"I'd be happy to," Jerome said.

"Good," the people said. "There is a dragon who can breathe fire. He has a terrible smell. We would like to get rid of him. He has been burning up our houses."

"Fine," Jerome said, and the people took him to a dark hole in the side of a hill. "The dragon is in there," they said. Then they ran to hide behind a rock.

Jerome called out, "Dragon, come out at once! I am here to get rid of you."

The dragon put his head out of the hole. "Why?" he asked.

"You have been burning up the houses of the people," Jerome said.

"Well," the dragon said. "That's the way I am. I just can't help burning things."

"Why not burn something different?" Jerome asked.

"What is there to burn?" the dragon asked.

"Well," Jerome said. "How about burning garbage at the town garbage dump. There are piles and piles of it outside the town."

"Is it easy to burn?" asked the dragon.

"Well, no," Jerome said. "It's a little wet and hard to start."

"Good," said the dragon. "I like something hard to do. Take me to it."

So Jerome took the dragon to the garbage dump. The dragon looked around the dump. He soon was very busy burning the town garbage.

After that, some of the people began to say, "Maybe Jerome really is a prince."

But most of the people still had to laugh. "He's just a frog."

So they asked Jerome to do one more princely deed. "We want you to do something about the wizard in the dark wood. He does terrible things. Get rid of him for us. You take the road to the left."

So Jerome took the road. He soon came to a building that had no door and no windows. At the top was the wizard. "Who are you?" he asked in a mean voice.

"I'm the prince who does princely deeds," Jerome said.

The wizard said to himself, "That silly frog really thinks he is a prince." Then he shouted at Jerome, "What were you before you were a prince?"

"A frog," Jerome said. "What were you before you were a wizard?"

The wizard stood up. "Well," he said after a long time, "I must have been a boy."

"Oh," Jerome said. "Why did you stop?"

"Well, being a wizard looked as if it would be fun," the wizard said. "But it's not."

"That's too bad," Jerome said. "I'm sorry. Was it fun being a boy?"

"Oh," said the wizard. "Was it ever! Summer sun; winter snow and ice; secret code; and going down a hill so fast you couldn't stop. Oh, I wish I were a boy again!"

The wizard did not remember that when he wished for things, they really happened. The wizard suddenly was a boy with red hair. "I," shouted the boy, "am going to run down the hill so fast I can't stop!" And, in a second, he was gone.

When the people in the town heard that the wizard was gone, they felt that Jerome must really be a prince, even if he looked like a frog.

They gave him a little building made of green rock, with a pond close by. The pond was the best. It was green and full of bugs. Jerome was very happy there.

A Tadpole's Journal

We work with words.

careless   restless   spotless

weren't   haven't

capture   mixture

shirt   circles   dirt

bottle   eagle   bugle

Sound the words.

helpless

aren't

creatures

dirty

turtles

Sight word.

We can go to the zoo later.

Spring. At last, with a beat of my tail, I've made it out of my egg. I can already swim well in the cold, clear water. I can see tadpoles hatch from the other eggs.

Later. I'm still very tiny. I spend most of my time eating. The water has other creatures who also spend most of their time eating. And they like to eat tiny tadpoles like me.

Still later. Fish and turtles live in the middle of the pond. Water bugs and spiders live among the plants. A raccoon is watching me from along the edge. And then, there are the creatures that walk on two legs. There is no place that's safe. I am helpless.

Summer. My back legs just grow and grow. They help me swim and get away from the raccoon and the other creatures. Fish and turtles swallow the other tadpoles whole. Water bugs and spiders eat them, too.

Later. There aren't many full-grown frogs here. The pond wasn't safe for them. The creatures got many of them. Others got too old and couldn't take care of themselves. Sometimes, I feel helpless.

Much later. I'm a full-grown frog now, and I have to eat bugs and take care of myself. Oh, yes — I found a mate. My mate has laid eggs, and from those eggs will hatch many tadpoles. They will have to take care of themselves with the turtles and spiders. The water in the pond is very dirty. It's dirty because the creatures who walk on two legs throw things into it. Even in the middle of the pond, there is garbage. It's hard for frogs to live for very long in dirty water.

Make a Home for a Frog

We work with words.

thicken   darken   fallen

bottoms   rubber   channel

Sound the words.

dampen

pebbles

soil

Sight word.

The fish are in the aquarium.

96

One way to learn about frogs is to keep one for a while. First, build the frog a good home that's half land and half water. You'll need an aquarium with a top, different size pebbles, sand, soil, plants, and water.

Next, make a wall across the bottom of the aquarium with pebbles. On one side will be the land; on the other side, the water.

Fill in the bottom of the land side with pebbles, sand, and soil. Put in plants. Now, fill the other half of the aquarium with fresh water. Dampen the soil and dampen the plants. Put some pebbles and a big rock in the water for the frog to sit on.

Keep the water clean, and always give the frog live bugs to eat.

There is much to be learned by keeping a frog. But you must pick your frog with care. It would not be good to keep some frogs in an aquarium. You need to know some facts about frogs.

Frog Facts

Some live in trees.

Some snore.

One kind of frog makes a sound like a dog.

Another makes a noise like a sheep.

Some frogs grow as big as a cat. Some are smaller as frogs than they were as tadpoles.

The skin of a frog may give off poison. To take care of itself, a frog will poison other animals — even people. The poison of one frog is so strong, it can give you a bad burn.

A frog will eat other frogs, snakes, fish, bugs, or almost anything that's alive and can fit into its mouth. A big frog will eat a small bird. Frogs swallow their food whole.

A frog can sing with its mouth shut. To sing, it makes air go in and out of its throat.

Fred Frog says, "Just look at my fine clothes. Don't I look like a prince?" Some people who are keeping frogs really do put clothes on them!

In winter, a frog will sleep in the mud at the bottom of a pond. It will use its skin to breathe.

Frogs can jump very far.

A frog can live no more than 15 years.

Almost all frogs hatch from eggs.

After you have had the frog for some time and have learned from it, let it go in a place where it will be happy.

UP, UP, and AWAY

Safe Simon

Before you fly, Safe Simon says:

1. Check the weather and the wind.

2. Check the balloon for safety.

3. Bring a map and a radio set.

4. Wear safe gear.

Keep in touch with your ground workers and take care! See you in the clouds!

To find the balloon center nearest you, write:
The Balloon Federation of America
Suite 610
806 Fifteenth Street, N.W.
Washington, D.C. 20005

The best way of travel,
    if you aren't in any hurry at all,
    if you don't care where you are
       going,
    if you don't like to use your legs,
    if you want to *see* everything quite
       clearly,
    if you don't want to be annoyed at
       all by any choice of directions,
is in a balloon.

by William Pène du Bois

Why Does a Balloon Go Up?

We work with words.

doom　broom

dreamer　leader　farmer

Sound the words.

balloons

burner

Sight word.

Balloons may be filled

with <u>helium</u>.

In 1783, two men from Europe may have made the first hot-air balloon. Their name was Montgolfier.

If you blow up a balloon and put it in water, it will stay on top of the water. The air in the balloon weighs less than the water.

But, if you fill the balloon with something that weighs less than air, it will go off the ground. Helium is a gas that weighs less than air. If you buy a balloon at a fair, it may be filled with helium.

Scientists use big gas balloons full of helium to study the weather.

When the bag is filled with gas, a balloon will lift off the ground. To go down, the pilot will let some gas out of the bag. To go up, the pilot will throw a bag of sand out of the cabin. Then the balloon weighs less.

When the bag is filled with hot air, a balloon will lift off the ground. This balloon uses a burner to heat air for the bag. To go up, the pilot will turn the burner up. To go down, the pilot will pull a string that will open the bag at the top and let out some hot air. Then the balloon comes back to the ground.

Scientists don't use balloons with hot air in them much. People do use them for fun.

In 1783, two friends of the Montgolfiers flew in a balloon. They may have been the first people to fly.

John Wise, Balloonist

We work with words.

			Sound the words.
hopeful	thankful		careful
twenty	ninety	fifty	safety
crew	drew	few	flew
grown	frown	blown	flown

Sight words.

The first time I saw a <u>balloonist</u>
was in <u>Europe</u>.

One day, John Wise read a story in the paper about some people who had flown in a balloon in Europe. John Wise had never even seen a balloon, but he made up his mind to build one.

He wanted to build a big balloon that could carry him. He didn't care how long it took; he wanted to fly.

It took more than ten years of careful work for him to do it, but at last John Wise did fly. He went up in a gas balloon that he had built himself and he landed in safety. But that short trip was just the start of his adventures. He built new and better balloons. The balloonist flew again and again.

Wise was the first balloonist to take off for a long trip across the United States. He had made a careful plan for the safety of his trip. He took three other people with him.

They had food and water, and they took some mail. Wise said he would take it to another city.

They flew a very long way. Then, when the balloon was over a lake, a storm came up. There was a heavy fog, and the wind blew very hard. The balloon had flown so close to the water that Wise and the others threw everything out of the balloon. They had to be careful to stay in the air.

When at last they were over land again, they still could not stop. Then the balloon flew into a tree, and the wild ride was at an end. They had made it to safety.

Wise did not go as far as he wanted, but he had flown farther in the air than anyone had before him.

When he was 71 years old, he wanted to take another long balloon trip. But his balloon went into some fog over a lake, and no one ever saw the balloon or John Wise again.

Where Would the Wind Take You?

If you took off in a balloon, where would the wind take you? Here is how you can find out.

Get a balloon filled with helium and tie a piece of cloth to it. At the end of the cloth, tie a note that tells your name, address, and the date when you let the balloon go. Someone may find your balloon and return it to you.

Let your balloon go on a nice day. There will be wind far up in the sky to move it along. Get some friends to do this with you. You can find out whose balloon goes farther and whose is found first.

Sarah's Balloon Center

We work with words.

south   bound

instead   handle   surprise

forgot   cornet   numbers

Sound the words.

clouds

basket

center

Sight words.

Are you <u>sure</u> that's

<u>Sarah's</u> balloon?

In 1799, Jeanne Garnerin became the first woman to fly alone in a balloon.

110

Hello! Welcome to Sarah's Balloon Center. I hear you want to learn to balloon. You'll love it! A little practice, and you'll be up there all alone in the clouds, and you'll know there's really no other way to go.

The first thing you need to know is how to blow up a balloon. We do that with this burner from the balloon basket. We want to put this balloon out on the ground so that the hot air from the burner will blow into the mouth of the balloon. Be sure the ropes of the basket are on the balloon. We won't get very far if we don't check that.

I love to watch balloons as they start to blow up. They stretch and wave hello just like big animals.

It takes awhile for a balloon to fill. While we wait, let's talk about being safe in a balloon.

1. Always check your balloon for leaks.
2. Fix any leaks you find.
3. Make sure your burner has gas.
4. Be sure your ropes are on the basket.
5. Watch the wind and the clouds.
6. Take a map with you when you fly.
7. Keep in touch with your friends on the ground.

I've made a check of this balloon, so it's ready to go. Do you want to work the burner? The burner makes quite a noise, doesn't it? That's how it tells us everything is fine. Up we go! Hello, clouds! Did you miss me?

EARTHWORM AND BIG EAGLE

We work with words.

tension   revision

pilots   level   bugle

ragtime   earthquake   airplane

understood   sunflowers

care   spare

Sound the words.

decision

eagle

earthworm

somewhere

hare

hounds

Sight words.

Rita Mendoza and her aunt
were looking toward the sky.

Hare and hounds is a game that balloonists have played for a long time. One balloon is the hare. It takes off and is blown away on the wind. The other balloons are the hounds. They give the hare time to land somewhere and then take off after it. The hounds must find the hare and then land as close to it as they can.

"Earthworm, this is Big Eagle."

"Okay, go ahead, Big Eagle."

"We see you, Earthworm. We're on our way down."

Rita Mendoza watched the big red balloon as it came toward her. She and her Aunt Rosa were help-

ing Rita's parents practice for a hare and hounds race.

Rita and her aunt played the hare. They hid the car in a field far downwind from the balloon and then called the Mendozas on the radio. Then they waited for the voice on the radio to say, "We see you, Earthworm."

Rita watched the balloon as it rose and fell in the air. Her parents were looking for a good wind so that they could land close to the hare.

"Who wants to be an earthworm?" said Rita to herself. "All earthworms do is sit and wait and watch. Up there is where all the fun is."

The balloon landed just a few yards away. The Mendozas had become good hounds. They got nearer every time.

Rita was very quiet while they packed up the balloon. She wanted a chance to be in the race. She had flown many times, but only two could be in the race. Rita's father saw how quiet she was, and he made a decision.

The day of the race was warm and clear. The wind blew from almost everywhere. The person who won would have to be a good balloonist.

There were about fifty hounds in the race. When they were all ready to go, Rita felt nervous. "Why should I be nervous?" she asked herself. "I'm just an earthworm. Earthworms stay on the ground."

Suddenly, the hare was off. Soon the hounds would take off, too.

"Okay, Earthworm," said her father. "In you go." Rita couldn't believe what she heard. She was going to race!

A horn blew, and the hounds took off. Rita's mother kept the burner turned up, and they rose quickly. Rita had been a hare, and she had learned to hide. She looked now for something that would tell her where the hare was hidden. It had to be somewhere.

Then, downwind, she saw a hill with some trees on it. "The hare is behind that hill," she shouted.

"How do you know?" her mother asked.

"I don't know, but I've been a hare. That's where I would be if I wanted to hide," Rita said.

"Okay!" shouted her mother. "Let's go."

117

They began to look for a good wind to carry them toward the hill. It wasn't easy, but they found it. Rita's mother pulled the cord. Air blew out of the bag, and down they went. Now they were in a good wind. It blew them toward the hill. And there, in a field hidden behind the trees, was the hare. It was just where Rita had said it would be.

"There it is! Let's go down!" Rita's mother said as she pulled the cord again. They landed about fifty yards from the hare.

Then they waited and watched the other balloons land. Only one other balloon landed nearer than they did. They had almost won their very first race!

This time, Rita wasn't quiet while they packed up the balloon. She had a lot to say. She told about the race again and again. But something was on her mind. She said, "You shouldn't have let me take your place."

"I made a decision," her father said. "I knew you could do it. We needed someone who could find the hare and ride the wind. You were a hound who could think like a hare. You were an earthworm who flew like an eagle."

WHO HAS SEEN THE WIND?

Who has seen the wind?
  Neither I nor you;
But when the leaves hang trembling,
  The wind is passing through.

Who has seen the wind?
  Neither you nor I;
But when the trees bow down their heads
  The wind is passing by.

Runways

Running for the Record

We work with words.

hitter   dipper   hidden

brush   brass   break

forgot   ankle   handle

Sound the words.

runners

broke

surprise

Sight words.

Sabina Chebichi is good at running.

This is in style.

122

A Barefoot Runner. Sabina Chebichi, who was just fourteen years old at the time, ran her first race in a new style. She didn't have money to buy track clothes, so she had on a slip and ran barefoot.

But this girl of fourteen could really run. To the surprise of everyone, she beat all the women in the race.

Sabina Chebichi was so fast in that race that they asked her to go to another city in her country and run in a big race there. And they bought her track clothes so she would not have to run barefoot and in her slip again. Then they gave her a free ride to the other city. Sabina won that race, too, and was asked to run for her country in other races.

A Surprise Win. Mary Decker was tiny for a girl of fifteen, and sometimes that made trouble for her. She was to run in a race for women, but one of the men who check to see that people don't get in the wrong race said she was too little to run in the race with women. To his surprise, he was told Mary Decker was to run in that race. Mary surprised everyone in that race, as she beat the women and broke a record, too.

Mary is one of the better track runners in this country.

Young Man on the Run

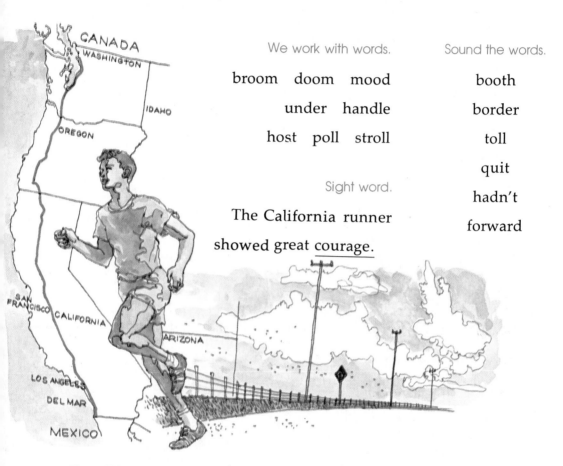

We work with words.

broom   doom   mood

under   handle

host   poll   stroll

Sound the words.

booth

border

toll

quit

hadn't

forward

Sight word.

The California runner showed great <u>courage</u>.

Jim Dunn was a long-distance runner with great courage. During the summer that he was sixteen years old, he ran 2,800 kilometers (1,750 miles) from Mexico to Canada. Part of the story of this boy of sixteen is told here.

125

We Get Ready

I had always wanted to go to a faraway place and also wanted to make something out of my running. So I had the idea of doing two things at one time by running to a faraway place.

As the summer of 1973 began, I went to Mom and told her what was on my mind. I wanted to run from Mexico to Canada. "Why not?" she said. She would follow me in our camper with food and clothes for the trip. My trip would take me into California, Oregon, and Washington.

We Leave Home — Twice

On the morning I began this run, we took the camper to the border of Mexico. The plan was for me to run about 30 kilometers (about 19 miles) that day, from the border back to my home. I didn't want to push too hard and make my legs hurt the first day.

I began to run. After a while, I began to
wonder why I was doing this. I was very tired
when we got to our home, and I wanted to quit.

Canada was so far away, I turned the idea of
what I was doing over and over in my mind. At
last, I got up my courage to go on, and the next
morning I began to run again.

My plan was to run alone. Mom would then
meet me with the camper at the end of each day.
Sometimes, she would bring me lunch or a
drink while I was on the road.

I asked myself if I would have the courage to
make it all the way from Mexico to Canada.

Days on the Road

Each day, I ran a little more. Most of the time, I was happy to be outside on the road. One morning, a man I hadn't seen before came by. He reached out from his car and gave me a lunch. Mom had sent it forward with him.

After about six weeks, my legs began to hurt. I had to stop now and then to rest my legs.

Sometimes, the hot sun made me very tired. On one such day, I was running toward a beach. Suddenly, as I ran over low hills, there was a loud noise over my head. I heard it again and again. Was someone out to have fun, or out to get me? Or did my mind just play a trick? I didn't know. But I got over those hills as fast as I could.

The End of the Long State

It took me many days to get from the bottom to the top of California. Crossing the border into Oregon, I felt very proud of myself. I was happy because I hadn't quit. I looked forward to telling everyone what I had done. But Mom was the only one there.

Trouble at a Bridge

I had been looking forward to crossing the bridge into Washington. The bridge was 6 kilometers (4 miles) long, and it was the only way of crossing the river into Washington. At the tollbooth, I got a surprise. The rules did not allow runners on the bridge.

I had to cross. I couldn't quit now. I had to get the man in the tollbooth on my side.

I told him that I had run over 2,200 kilometers (1,400 miles), and that I had to run across that bridge. The man wanted to follow the rules. But at last he gave in and let me by the tollbooth.

I was very happy, because if that man hadn't let me cross the bridge, I would have had to swim. And I really had the courage to swim the river that time, all the way across it.

Reaching Canada

On September 7, the sky was clear blue, the way I love it. Running down the road, I could see hills up ahead, and I knew the hills were in Canada. I would be at the border soon.

I saw the Peace Arch from a long way off. The Peace Arch is at the border between the United States and Canada. I ran fast, and then I was there. I was in Canada. I had to stand under the Peace Arch for a while to catch my breath. I had run 2,800 kilometers (1,750 miles). I was alone. I had done it.

The Henry "Box" Brown Story

We work with words.

wage   ginger   age

spare   flare   care

Sound the words.

danger

dare

die

Sight words.

He went by train from Virginia to

Philadelphia.

131

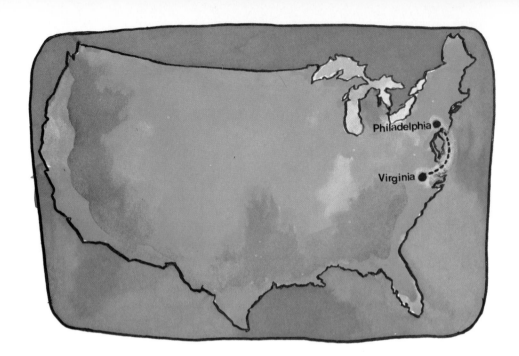

Running Away

Some people run for fun, and some run to win a race or to set a record. But others run to get away from something. Henry Brown was such a man. He was a slave in Virginia in 1848. Henry Brown knew there were black people in the North who were free, and they could live and work where they wanted. But Henry belonged to another man. He had to work for this man, and he got no pay for his work. If he ran away, there was great danger that people would catch him and bring him back. They might beat him.

This is his story, the way he told it.

I had been a slave in Virginia too long, and made up my mind to run away. I wanted to go north and be a free man. But I could not do it alone. Who would dare to help me? At last, I found someone by the name of Smith. He was a white man. Smith and I worked out a plan. I would build a box of wood. Then he would mail the box, with me in it, to his friends in Philadelphia.

It was my only chance. Did I dare to run away to the city of Philadelphia? What if it broke open and someone saw me? It was very bad for a slave to dare to run away and then be found. Would I live? Would I die? I didn't know. I wanted to be free, but I didn't want to die. I had to take a chance on the danger.

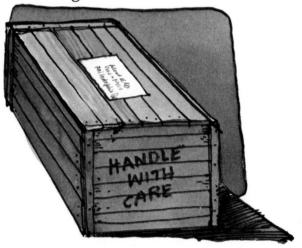

A Free Man

The time came to run away. There was room in the box for a little food and water. Smith put me in the box. Then he put the top on. He took it to the train.

On my box were the words, "This Side Up" and "Handle with Care." But at the station my box was set upside down. I found myself on my head. What a terrible feeling of helplessness! Just then, the train came. I landed head up in the box.

134

I knew I would go from the train to a ship, and I could only hope the workers would handle my box with care. But I landed upside down again. It hurt! I broke out in a sweat.

Even in my state of helplessness, I didn't dare make a sound. The danger was great. If someone found me, I would die. A cold sweat came over me. I had the feeling I was going to die upside down in the box. Then two men began to move my box to sit on it. I was no longer upside down, and the hurt feeling went away.

We went north for two days. Then my box went by wagon to Philadelphia, and it was left at the Philadelphia train station. The next day, I felt people put it on a wagon and move it into a house.

At first, people did not talk or handle the box. Again that terrible feeling of helplessness came over me. Who would be there? Would they really help a slave from Virginia? Then someone asked, "Henry Brown, are you alive in there?"

"All is well," I said. Quickly someone took the top off of the box. A smile was on my face, for the danger was over. I was free from the box. But most of all, I was now a free man.

WATERWAYS

The Greatest Dive

treasure   pleasure   sure

editor   inventor

benches   blues   sandwiches

weigh   eight   freight

deepest   tallest

measure

sailor

crutches

eighty

greatest

inches

skull

wrung

Eddie bragged that he
never practiced the ukulele.

Here I am on crutches, with my arms and skull hurt, too. I'll live, I suppose, but I can never dive again. That's why I had to start this ladder store.

I was working for a fair run by Mr. Miller last summer. My long dive got a lot of people to come to the show. They called me "Billy the Fish." With a wave to the people, I would dive from a ladder of twenty-five feet into a tank ten feet deep. No one could measure up to me. I was the greatest.

139

Then Eddie La Breen came to town.

One night, I came up out of the tank, waiting to hear people clap. But I heard someone shout, "That's nothing! You should see Eddie La Breen in the show over on Green Street. He can dive twice as far into half as much water!"

I found out it was true. Eddie La Breen called himself "The Human Seal." He bragged that he could dive into less water than anybody in the world. He did his dive from fifty feet up into five feet of water. And Mr. Miller told me I would have no job if I couldn't do as well. But "The Human Seal" was not going to beat old "Billy the Fish" if I could help it.

Next, I put something new in my act. I put a little gas on top of the water and set it on fire. When I hit the tank, fire would splash everywhere. It gave the people a big surprise.

Then Eddie came to my show. "I can dive from 1,000 feet into a concrete tank," he bragged in a loud voice. "And I can do it while playing the ukulele and eating a steak sandwich."

"Why, when I was a boy," he said, "I would dive twenty-five feet off our house onto the ground when it had a little rain on it."

Eddie was good, but not that good. Eddie sent word that he was going to dive from 300 feet into 3 inches of water. "When I land, I won't even mess up that water with a wave," he said.

I had to practice hard to measure a better dive than Eddie. I got so I could dive into 2 inches of water from 264 feet up.

When Eddie made a still better dive than I did, I was a little put out. But I didn't give up. I told Mr. Miller to get me a heavy mat and put it in water all day. I had to practice every day. But I beat Eddie!

Eddie lost his job when I beat him. I heard he went to sea and became a sailor, so I had no idea he was there that terrible day.

I put my mat in water as always. But someone had wrung it out until it was nearly dry.

Later, I heard there was a sailor at the fair that night. He was playing a ukulele and eating a steak sandwich. Only Eddie would have wrung out my mat like that.

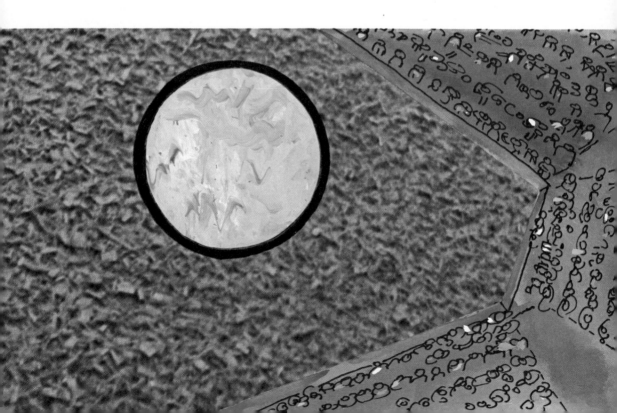

When I first hit the mat that night, it looked like my time had come. That was almost a year ago, and look at me — still on crutches, and my arms and skull still hurt.

I hear Eddie is back on the job here in town. I'm going to let Eddie make his greatest dive. And if it doesn't work out, well, I could use another man around the store.

People

clash   claim   click   cliffs

channel

A Cold Swim

There is one group of people who swim outside even on the coldest days of the year. Sometimes they have to chop the ice before they can jump in for a swim.

A Long Dive

Sam Hernandez likes to dive off the cliffs in Mexico. To clear the cliffs, he must push himself far out from the rock walls. When he gets to the water after his long fall, he is going very fast. He must go into the water and not hurt himself.

First Woman to Swim Channel

In 1926, this woman became the first woman to swim the English Channel. She swam the channel more quickly than any man had up to that time.

Watch the Sharks

In this aquarium, there is a very big tank filled with sea life of all kinds. People dive into the tank and hand out dinner to hungry turtles and fish. The people have to slap sharks who want more than their share!

Who Said It Couldn't Be Done?

We work with words.

playful   painful   watchful

dish   gift   film

Sound the words.

graceful

lap

cry

Sight words.

A <u>champion</u> goes to bed

at <u>eight</u> o'clock.

148

All the seats in the building were quickly filled that night. More than 3,000 people could not get into the hall.

Mr. and Mrs. Gould and some of their children took their places. "All these people have come to see Shane Gould set a record," said Mrs. Gould, looking nervous. "And many more people will be watching the race on TV."

A grin was on Mr. Gould's face. Sometimes he had helped her, but now Shane was on her own. And he knew she would do just fine.

Mr. Gould was very proud of Shane. After all, how many young girls had set six world records? But he knew that this was the race Shane wanted to win most of all.

Shane was alone in a small room. She was working with her rope, to warm up for the race.

Suddenly, someone ran into Shane's room. The race for women was being pushed ahead! "Quick!" she called to Shane. "Your race is about to begin!"

Shane looked up from her rope. She was not at all happy to hear this. She wanted more time to get ready for the race. She needed to have some time alone before she swam.

"Why didn't they tell me?" she asked. She took a deep breath. Then she went out to the pool, looking as if she were about to cry.

The race began. In the first lap, Shane seemed to be swimming too slowly. People said, "She made too slow a start!" They wanted Shane to win and set a new record very much.

On the return lap, Shane pulled ahead. Her strong arms pushed her body across the water. She reached out to touch the wall at the finish. Then they called out that she had set a new world record.

What makes a champion? For one thing, no one ever had to tell Shane to get into the water. As a baby, she would cry when her bath was over. At two, she could swim underwater with her eyes open. She was always very happy in the water.

When she was six, a coach began training her. He showed her how to keep fit. With the help of her coach, her swimming became graceful and fast. She won her first prize when she was still quite young. Each coach helped her learn just a little more.

Shane liked swimming. Her body was graceful. Shane felt good being in the water.

But there is more to being a champion. Shane went to practice every day and swam lap, after lap, after lap. Sometimes the water was very cold.

Shane could not do many of the things her friends did. She couldn't stay up late to watch TV. Every night, she went to bed at eight to be ready to swim the next day. And every day, she got up at four. At times, Shane had to sleep in the day when there was more than one race. It was easy to sleep on such days.

Good eating was another part of good training. Her food was made with great care. She could not eat just anything.

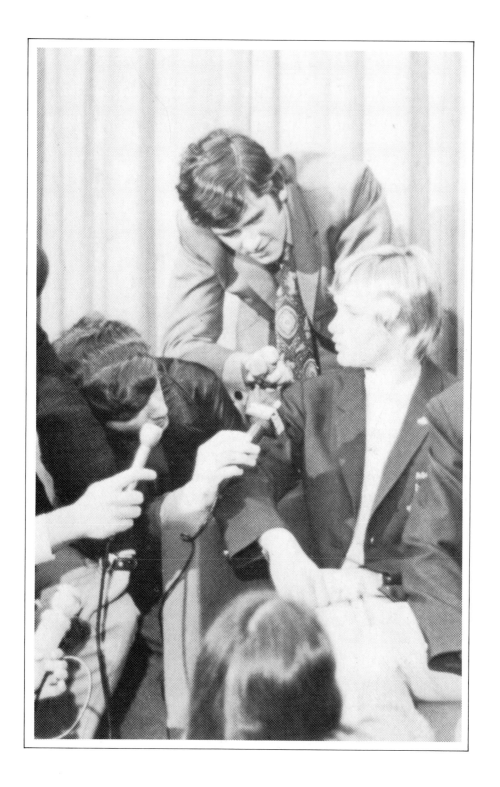

But Shane was really doing what she wanted to do most. She did it so well that she got to go to many parts of the world. She got to meet many important people. Shane was on the TV, and her picture was in the paper many times.

ACKNOWLEDGMENTS

For permission to adapt and reprint copyrighted materials, grateful acknowledgment is made to the following:

Lois Kalb Bouchard, author, and McIntosh and Otis, Inc., for "The Boy Who Wouldn't Talk" adapted from *The Boy Who Wouldn't Talk* by Lois Kalb Bouchard, copyright © 1969 by Lois Kalb Bouchard. Doubleday & Company, Inc., publisher. Reprinted by permission of the author.

Crown Publishers, Inc., for "The Greatest Dive" taken from *A Treasury of American Folklore* edited by B. A. Botkin. Copyright © 1944, 1972 by B. A. Botkin. Used by permission of Crown Publishers, Inc.

Macmillan Publishing Company, Inc., for "The Henry 'Box' Brown Story" adapted with permission of Macmillan Publishing Co., Inc., from *Black Slave Narratives* by John F. Bayliss. Copyright © 1970 by John F. Bayliss.

Newsweek, Inc., for "A Barefoot Runner" adapted from "Kenya: The Barefoot Contestant," copyright © 1973 by Newsweek, Inc., and for "A Surprise Win" adapted from "Nice Girls Finish First," copyright © 1974 by Newsweek, Inc. All rights reserved. Reprinted by permission.

Parents' Magazine Press for "Jerome" adapted from *Jerome* by Philip Ressner. Text copyright © 1967 by Philip Ressner. By permission of Parents' Magazine Press.

Playboy, for the poem "Not Me" by Shel Silverstein; originally appeared in *Playboy* Magazine; copyright © 1960 by Playboy.

Sterling Publishing Company, Inc., for "Who Said It Couldn't Be Done?" adapted from *Swimming the Shane Gould Way* by Shirley Gould. Copyright © 1972 by Shirley Gould. Used by permission of Sterling Publishing Co., Inc.

Time Inc., for "Young Man on the Run" condensed and adapted from the original story by Jim Dunn which appeared in the August 12, 1974, issue of *Sports Illustrated*. Reprinted by permission of author and publisher. © Time Inc.

The Viking Press, Inc., for "The Best Way of Travel" reprinted from *The Twenty-One Balloons* by William Pène Du Bois, copyright © 1947 by William Pène Du Bois. Reprinted by permission of The Viking Press, Inc.

Grateful acknowledgment is made to the following for reproduction of photographs and color transparencies on the pages indicated:

The Bettmann Archive, Inc. 38; Robert Ebeling, Balloon Federation of America 101; J.C. Helmer, Follett Publishing Company 34; Historical Pictures Service, Chicago 32, 33; Gill Kenny, Tucson 53, 54; Naval Historical Foundation, Washington, D.C. 36, 37; Pictorial Parade, Inc. 26; Marilyn Sherburne, Kerr-McGee Swim Team 148; SkipperLiner Houseboat Company, La Crosse, Wisconsin 54; Dick Stamberg, Balloon Federation of America 101; Sterling Publishing Company, Inc. 151, 152, 153, 154, 155, 156, 157, 158; Wide World Photos, Inc., 100.

Grateful acknowledgment is made to the following for illustrations on the pages indicated:

Margot Apple 21, 22, 23; Ellen Appleby 24; Ellen Blonder 46, 47, 48, 110, 111, 112, 113, 114, 115, 116, 117, 118, 119, 120; Eulala Conner 8, 9, 10, 11, 13, 14, 122, 124; Bert Dodson 121, 131, 132, 133, 135, 136; Pamela Ford 17, 18, 19, 20; Hal Frenck 125, 126, 127, 128, 129, 130; Jon Goodell 25, 44; John Gumm 7; Connie Hwang 7; William Mathison 81; Lyle Miller 27, 28, 29, 30, 35; Steve Reoutt 49, 50, 51, 52, 55, 57, 59, 60, 61, 62, 63, 64, 137, 145, 146, 147; Karen Scott 39, 40, 41, 42; Bill Shires 65, 66, 68, 69, 70, 71, 73, 74, 75, 76, 77, 78, 79, 80; Rachel Thompson 7; Karen Tucker 103, 104, 105; Connie Warton 102, 106, 107, 108, 109, 138, 139, 141, 142, 143, 144; Gordon Willman 82, 83, 84, 86, 88, 89, 90, 91, 92, 93, 94, 95, 96.